Johann Strauss (Son)

The Blue Danube / An der schönen blauen Donau
Op. 314

Artist's Life / Künstlerleben
Op. 316

Edited by / Herausgegeben von
Richard Clarke

T0081282

EULENBURG

EAS 184
ISBN 978-3-7957-6584-2
ISMN 979-0-2002-2603-4

© 2013 Ernst Eulenburg & Co GmbH, Mainz
for Europe excluding the British Isles
Ernst Eulenburg Ltd, London
for all other countries
Edition based on Eulenburg Study Score ETP 822 & 870
CD ℗ 1988 & 1991 Naxos Rights International Ltd
CD © 2013 Ernst Eulenburg Ltd, London

Ernst Eulenburg Ltd
48 Great Marlborough Street
London W1F 7BB

Contents / Inhalt

Tempo di Valse

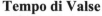

Preface

The Blue Danube
Composed: 1866/67
First performance: 15 February 1867 in Vienna (choir version) /
10 March 1867 (orchestra version)
both conducted by the composer
Original publisher: C.A.Spina, Vienna, 1867
Instrumentation: Piccolo, 2 Flutes, 2 Oboes, 2 Clarinets, 2 Bassoons –
4 Horns, 2 Trumpets, 3 Trombones – Timpani, Triangle, 2 Drums,
Cymbals – Harp – Strings
Duration: ca. 9 minutes

Artist's Life
Composed: 1867
First performance: 18 March 1867 in Vienna
conducted by the composer
Original publisher: C.A.Spina, Vienna, 1867
Instrumentation: Piccolo, Flute, 2 Oboes, 2 Clarinets, 2 Bassoons –
4 Horns, 2 Trumpets, 3 Trombones – Timpani, Triangle, 2 Drums,
Cymbals – Strings
Duration: ca. 9 minutes

Behind every successful man is a strong woman – so indeed it was with Johann Strauss (Jr.), only in his case it was not one but three or four instead. Exactly what significance from a musical point of view the three wives – who tenderly called their Johann, Jean or Jeany – must have been destined for can be gathered from this comment by Norbert Linke: 'Undoubtedly *Der lustige Krieg* ['The Merry War'] is Johann's and Lily's operetta – as *Die Fledermaus* ['The Bat'] was Jean's und Jetty's work, *Der Zigeunerbaron* ['The Gypsy Baron'] will be the operetta by Jeany and Adele.'[1] Still, Johann Strauss could rely not only on the support of his three partners; early on his mother Anna had also bolstered him. If at first she also could show little enthusiasm for the future plans of her eldest, then his father was to prove above all an implacable opponent of the career sought by his son.

---

[1] Norbert Linke: *Johann Strauß (Sohn) in Selbstzeugnissen und Bilddokumenten* (Reinbek, 1982), 128. The entire biographical profile is based on this monograph.

But once Strauss (Sr.) finally separated from wife and family, the then barely 18-year-old Johann was declared head of the family, and mother Anna at last gave her support to Johann's professional ambitions – still against his father's will and who even attempted in court to regain influence over his son. The death of Joseph Lanner, who for many years had represented the father's greatest competition, provided the impetus for Johann's own move that very year into professional popular music. After sufficient preparation time, Strauss endeavoured the following year to get a *Musiklicenz* from the Vienna municipality in order to be able to follow in Lanner's steps. The first appearance with his specially assembled orchestra took place – only a few weeks after the consent – in October 1844. The evening turned out to be a complete success, spectators and press cheered and Franz Wiest declared in the newspaper *Der Wanderer*: 'Good Night, Lanner! Good Evening, Strauss Senior! Good Morning, Strauss Junior!'[2] Numerous wildly acclaimed engagements ensued and inevitably made the son into one of his father's greatest rivals. Despite his triumph, however, Johann Strauss (Jr.) succeeded in rising to the pinnacle of the waltz empire only after his father's death in 1849. This now unrestricted domination of the entertainment sector he had owed not least to the fact that he could pursue further a pathway left behind by his father. Realised first of all was the merging of the two Strauss orchestras. Ultimately, the Haslinger publishing house volunteered as contractual partner, though on less favourable terms than those his father had received. In 1852, the management of the royal court-ball music was assigned him – in rotation with Philipp Fahrbach. But it was not until 11 years later that he was granted the long sought-after title of *k.k.Hofballmusikdirektor* [Imperial-Royal Court-Ball Director], initiated by his father.

The immense scale of his responsibilities left its mark on the young *Kapellmeister* and composer. Thus, for health reasons he was forced in 1853 to take it easier, and his brother Josef was tapped to join the family enterprises. However, as early as a year later contacts to Russia yielded a contract for a long-term concert series in Pavlovsk near St Petersburg where Johann was to spend the summers from 1856. As of 1862 the family music business was also no longer conceivable without the third Strauss brother Eduard, and the orchestra management was apportioned between the two younger brothers, whilst to the composer Johann his newly gained time now came in useful.

After a liaison with the Russian Olga Smirnitzki had broken up at the beginning of 1860 and she had left with the words 'Forget your disloyal hobgoblin […]',[3] Johann made his first marriage with Henriette von Treffz in the summer of 1862. The singer not only occasionally stood by his side on the stage, but backstage she also proved to be an indispensable helpmeet. 'She was his secretary, bookkeeper, tour agent, music copyist and nurse. She made a comfortable home for him and thus achieved the psychological feat of gradually relieving her Jean of such an intense mother fixation and strengthening his artistic self-confidence. It is questionable whether so sublime a succession of "familiar waltzes" and Jean's metamorphosis to "Operetta King" would indeed have come about without Jetty's influence […].'[4]

---

[2] ibid., 35
[3] ibid., 66
[4] ibid., 75

The year 1867 finally brought Strauss one of his greatest successes. After the initial, still somewhat muted, reception of the waltz *An der schönen blauen Donau* ['To the Beautiful Blue Danube'] at the Viennese premiere in February, Strauss's appearance at the Paris World Exhibition set off such excitement that for months concert-goers now demanded 'the Danube waltz' with unbroken enthusiasm. The triumphal march around the entire world was no longer to be held back.

The deaths of his mother and brother Josef only three years later marked a decisive point. Eduard was now responsible alone for managing the Strauss orchestra, and Johann made off for new shores: the successful performances of Offenbach's *Die schöne Helena* ['The Beautiful Helena'] had aroused Strauss's ambition to try his hand at the heretofore unexplored world of operetta.

Besides countless guest appearances that even led the couple to America, composing operetta now assumed an ever-greater importance in Strauss's life. Henriette's sudden death in 1878 sent Strauss reeling; she it was who had provided him with 'operetta fame and had promoted his world-wide renown by managing sensational art tours'.[5]

Yet, the widower did not long remain single. Less than two months after the death of his first wife he married the considerably younger Ernestine Henriette Angelika Dittrich, called Lily – admittedly their 'acquaintanceship' had already been in place for some time previously. And soon enough a new wind was blowing in the Strauss house, because his new wife operated far less in the background than Henriette had done. In particular, the range of parts became more complex. Thus, 'formal palace revolutions and coups d'etat took place in Igel Strasse, and in the two ground-floor rooms intrigue parts were enacted that mostly were much more entertaining for the uninvolved spectators than the subsequently chosen librettos.'[6] However, the marriage with Lily did not last long. She ended the relationship in 1882 and the divorce took place within the same year.

The deserted Johann consoled himself straightaway with the young widow Adele Deutsch, whom though he could marry only in 1887 – after he became a German citizen and converted to Protestantism in order to obtain the divorce from Lily, which had remained void according to strict Catholic principles. And even the third Frau Strauss tried to emphasize new features and ultimately established the association with the Hungarian Maurus Jókai that at least produced the first sketches for the *Zigeunerbaron*. In the last years of his life composition of operettas and dance music again dominated Strauss's everyday work. The completion of a ballet eluded him. Strauss died in the summer of 1899.

Even after his orientation to operetta, Strauss still continued to compose concertante music. His father's example could still be recognized above all in the formal layout of the waltz compositions.[7] Still, Strauss (Jr.) pursued new stylistic paths: 'From the waltz to be danced

[5]   ibid., 120
[6]   ibid., 126f
[7]   cf. Marion Linhardt: [Article], 'Johann Baptist Strauß', in: *MGG*[2P], Vol.16 (Kassel, etc., 2006), cols. 33f

came a waltz to be listened to.'[8] The waltzes absorbed ever more clearly symphonic traits. These can be discerned especially in the motivic work. But the orchestral setting is also – in advance of the clichés of contemporary opera productions – increasingly more demanding. The waltz *An der schönen blauen Donau* succeeded as one of Strauss's greatest masterpieces. Ever since the incredible triumph that Strauss experienced a few months after the premiere during the Paris World Exhibition in 1867, the work has been breaking all records, and up to the present day it is impossible to imagine the concert repertoire without the 'Blue Danube Waltz'. The waltz *Künstlerleben* ['Artist's Life'] dates from this same successful year.

Sandra Borzikowski
Translation: Margit L. McCorkle

[8] ibid., col. 33

Vorwort

An der schönen blauen Donau
komponiert: 1866/67
Uraufführung: 15. Februar 1867 in Wien (Chorfassung) /
10. März 1867 (Orchesterfassung)
unter der Leitung des Komponisten
Originalverlag: C. A. Spina, Wien, 1867
Orchesterbesetzung: Piccolo, 2 Flöten, 2 Oboen, 2 Klarinetten, 2 Fagotte –
4 Hörner, 2 Trompeten, 3 Posaunen – Pauken, Triangel, 2 Trommeln,
Becken – Harfe – Streicher
Spieldauer: etwa 9 Minuten

Künstlerleben
komponiert: 1867
Uraufführung: 18. März 1867 in Wien
unter der Leitung des Komponisten
Originalverlag: C. A. Spina, Wien, 1867
Orchesterbesetzung: Piccolo, Flöte, 2 Oboen, 2 Klarinetten, 2 Fagotte –
4 Hörner, 2 Trompeten, 3 Posaunen – Pauken, Triangel, 2 Trommeln,
Becken – Streicher
Spieldauer: etwa 9 Minuten

Hinter jedem erfolgreichen Mann steht eine starke Frau – so wohl auch bei Johann Strauß (Sohn), nur dass es bei ihm nicht eine, sondern gleich drei bzw. vier waren. Welche Bedeutung gerade auch in musikalischer Hinsicht den drei Ehefrauen – die ihren Johann liebevoll Jean bzw. Jeany nannten – zugedacht werden muss, lässt sich aus einer Bemerkung Norbert Linkes ablesen: „Zweifellos ist *Der lustige Krieg* Johanns und Lilys Operette – wie *Die Fledermaus* Jeans und Jettys Werk war, *Der Zigeunerbaron* die Operette von Jeany und Adele sein wird."[1] Doch Johann Strauß konnte sich nicht nur auf die Unterstützung seiner drei Partnerinnen verlassen, auch die Mutter Anna hatte ihrem Sohn schon früh den Rücken gestärkt. Konnte auch sie zunächst den Zukunftsplänen ihres Ältesten wenig Begeisterung entgegenbringen, so sollte sich vor allem der Vater als unerbittlicher Gegner der vom Sohn angestrebten musikalischen Laufbahn erweisen.

---

[1] Norbert Linke: *Johann Strauß (Sohn) in Selbstzeugnissen und Bilddokumenten*, Reinbek 1982, S. 128. Der gesamte biographische Abriss stützt sich auf diese Monographie.

Aber als Strauß (Vater) sich schließlich von Frau und Familie trennte, wurde der damals knapp 18-jährige Johann kurzerhand zum neuen Familienoberhaupt erklärt und Mutter Anna ergriff endlich Position für die beruflichen Ambitionen Johanns – nach wie vor gegen den Willen des Vaters, der sogar auf gerichtlichem Weg seinen Einfluss auf den Sohn wiederzuerlangen versuchte. Der Tod Joseph Lanners, der all die Jahre die größte Konkurrenz für den Vater dargestellt hatte, lieferte noch im gleichen Jahr die Initialzündung für den Schritt in die professionelle Unterhaltungsmusik. Nach ausreichender Vorbereitungszeit bemühte sich Strauß im folgenden Jahr um eine Lizenz beim Wiener Magistrat, um in Lanners Fußstapfen treten zu können. Der erste Auftritt mit dem eigens zusammengestellten Orchester erfolgte – nur wenige Wochen nach der Bewilligung – im Oktober des Jahres 1844. Der Abend erwies sich als voller Erfolg, Zuschauer und Presse jubelten und Franz Wiest konstatierte in der Zeitung *Der Wanderer*: „Gute Nacht Lanner! Guten Abend Strauß Vater! Guten Morgen Strauß Sohn!"[2] Zahlreiche frenetisch gefeierte Engagements folgten und machten den Sohn unweigerlich zu einem der größten Rivalen des Vaters. Trotz des Erfolges gelang es Johann Strauß (Sohn) jedoch erst nach dem Tod des Vaters im Jahr 1849 an die Spitze des Walzer-Imperiums aufzurücken. Diese nun uneingeschränkte Beherrschung des Unterhaltungssektors hatte er nicht zuletzt der Tatsache zu verdanken, dass er die vom Vater hinterlassenen Pfade weiter beschreiten konnte. Zunächst wurde die Zusammenlegung der beiden Strauß-Orchester realisiert. Schließlich bot sich das Verlagshaus Haslinger als Vertragspartner an, wenn auch zu schlechteren Konditionen als sie der Vater erhalten hatte. 1852 wurde ihm die Leitung der Hofball-Musiken – im Wechsel mit Philipp Fahrbach – übertragen. Den lang ersehnten, vom Vater initiierte Titel des „k. k. Hofballmusik-Director" wird er aber erst 11 Jahre später endlich führen dürfen.

Das immense Ausmaß an Verpflichtungen ging nicht spurlos an dem jungen Kapellmeister und Komponisten vorüber. So war er 1853 gezwungen, aus gesundheitlichen Gründen kürzer zu treten, und Bruder Josef wurde ausersehen, in das Familienunternehmen einzusteigen. Doch schon ein Jahr später brachten Kontakte nach Russland einen Vertrag für eine langjährige Konzertserie in Pawlowsk bei St. Petersburg ein, wo Johann Strauß ab 1856 die Sommer verbringen sollte. Seit 1862 war auch der dritte Strauß-Sprössling Eduard nicht mehr aus dem familiären Musikbetrieb wegzudenken und die Orchesterleitung wurde zwischen den beiden jüngeren Brüdern aufgeteilt, während die neu gewonnene Zeit nun dem Komponisten Johann Strauß zugute kam.

Nachdem eine Liaison mit der Russin Olga Smirnitzki Anfang des Jahres 1860 gescheitert war und sie sich mit den Worten „Vergiss Deinen ungetreuen Kobold ..."[3] verabschiedet hatte, ging Johann im Sommer 1862 seine erste Ehe mit Henriette von Treffz ein. Die Sängerin stand ihm nicht nur gelegentlich auf der Bühne zur Seite, auch im Hintergrund erwies sie sich als unverzichtbare Gefährtin. „Sie wurde seine Sekretärin, Buchhalterin, Tournee-Vorbereiterin, Noten-Kopiererin und – Krankenpflegerin. Sie schuf ihm ein behagliches Heim und brachte so das psychologische Kunststück fertig, ihren Jean von der so starken Mutterbindung allmählich abzulösen und sein künstlerisches Selbstbewusstsein zu stärken. Fraglich

---

[2] Ebda., S. 35.
[3] Ebda., S. 66.

ist, ob die so grandiose Reihe der ‚geflügelten Walzer' und Jeans Wandlung zum ‚Operetten-könig' ohne Jettys Einfluss je zustande gekommen wären ..."[4]

Das Jahr 1867 bescherte Strauß schließlich einen seiner größten Erfolge. Nach der zunächst noch etwas verhaltenen Aufnahme des Walzers *An der schönen blauen Donau* bei der Wiener Uraufführung im Februar, lösten Strauß' Auftritte auf der Pariser Weltausstellung eine solche Begeisterung aus, dass die Konzertbesucher nun über Monate hinweg mit ungebrochenem Eifer den „Donauwalzer" einforderten. Der Siegeszug um die ganze Welt war nicht mehr aufzuhalten.

Nur 3 Jahre später hinterließen der Tod der Mutter und des Bruders Josef einen tiefen Einschnitt. Eduard war nun allein für die Leitung der Strauß-Kapelle verantwortlich und Johann machte sich auf zu neuen Ufern: Die erfolgreichen Aufführungen von Offenbachs *Die schöne Helena* hatten Strauß' Ehrgeiz geweckt, sich selbst auf dem bisher unbekannten Terrain der Operette auszuprobieren.

Neben zahllosen Gastspielen, die das Ehepaar sogar nach Amerika führten, nahm nun das Operetten-Schaffen eine immer größere Bedeutung in Strauß' Leben ein. Der plötzliche Tod Henriettes im Jahr 1878 warf Strauß aus der Bahn, hatte sie ihm doch „zum Operetten-Ruhm verholfen und durch das Management sensationeller Kunstreisen seinen Weltruhm gefördert".[5]

Doch lange allein blieb der Witwer nicht. Nicht einmal zwei Monate waren seit dem Tod seiner ersten Frau vergangen als er die deutlich jüngere Ernestine Henriette Angelika Dittrich, Lily genannt, ehelichte – die „Bekanntschaft" hatte freilich schon länger bestanden. Und schon bald wehte ein neuer Wind im Hause Strauß, denn Strauß' neue Gattin agierte weit weniger im Hintergrund als Henriette es getan hatte. Insbesondere die Auswahl der Stücke gestaltete sich nicht einfach. So „fanden förmliche Palastrevolutionen und Staatsstreiche in der Igelgasse statt, und es wurden in den beiden Parterrezimmern Intrigenstücke aufgeführt, die für den unbeteiligten Zuschauer meist viel unterhaltender waren als die nachher ausgewählten Libretti."[6] Doch die Ehe mit Lily sollte nicht von langer Dauer sein. 1882 beendete sie die Beziehung und noch im gleichen Jahr erfolgte die Scheidung.

Der verlassene Johann tröstete sich unmittelbar mit der jungen Witwe Adele Deutsch, die er allerdings erst 1887 – nachdem er deutscher Reichsbürger geworden war und zum Protestantismus konvertierte, um die nach streng katholischen Grundsätzen unwirksame Scheidung von Lily zu erwirken – heiraten konnte. Und auch die dritte Frau Strauß versuchte neue Akzente zu setzen und stellte schließlich die Verbindung zum Ungarn Maurus Jókai her, die immerhin die ersten Entwürfe für den *Zigeunerbaron* hervorbrachte. In den letzten Lebensjahren bestimmte wieder die Komposition von Operetten und Tanzmusik Strauß' Arbeitsalltag. Die Vollendung eines Balletts blieb ihm versagt. Strauß stirbt im Sommer 1899.

---

[4] Ebda., S. 75.
[5] Ebda., S. 120.
[6] Ebda., S. 126f.

Auch nach seiner Hinwendung zur Operette, komponierte Strauß weiterhin konzertante Musik. Das Vorbild des Vaters lässt sich vor allem in der formalen Anlage der Walzerkompositionen noch erkennen.[7] Doch stilistisch beschreitet Strauß (Sohn) neue Wege: „Aus dem Walzer zum Tanzen wurde ein Walzer zum Zuhören."[8] Die Walzer tragen immer deutlichere symphonische Züge. Diese lassen sich insbesondere in der motivischen Arbeit feststellen. Aber auch der Orchestersatz wird – vor der Schablone der aktuellen Opernproduktionen – zunehmend anspruchsvoller. Mit dem Walzer *An der schönen blauen Donau* gelang Strauß eines seiner größten Meisterwerke. Spätestens seit dem unvorstellbaren Triumph, den Strauß wenige Monate nach der Uraufführung während der Pariser Weltausstellung 1867 erlebt, schlägt das Werk alle Rekorde und bis heute ist der *Donauwalzer* aus den Konzertprogrammen nicht wegzudenken. Der Walzer *Künstlerleben* entstammt dem gleichen Erfolgsjahr.

Sandra Borzikowski

---

[7] Vgl. Marion Linhardt: Art. „Johann Baptist Strauß", in: *MGG*²ᴾ, Bd. 16, Kassel, usw. 2006, Sp. 33f.
[8] Ebda., Sp. 33.

The Blue Danube

Johann Strauss
(1825–1899)
Op. 314

Introduction
Andantino

EAS 184

Edited by Richard Clarke
© 2013 Ernst Eulenburg Ltd, London
and Ernst Eulenburg & Co GmbH, Mainz

4

Tempo di Valse

Walzer I

12

Walzer III

Lebhaft

28

EAS 184

Walzer V
Eingang

EAS 184

Coda

40

Printed in China

Artist's Life

Johann Strauss
(1825–1899)
Op. 316

Introduction
Andante moderato

EAS 184

Edited by Richard Clarke
© 2013 Ernst Eulenburg Ltd, London
and Ernst Eulenburg & Co GmbH, Mainz

58

Tempo di Valse

Walzer I

Walzer III

Walzer IV

82

Walzer V

rit. % a tempo

84

Coda

a tempo

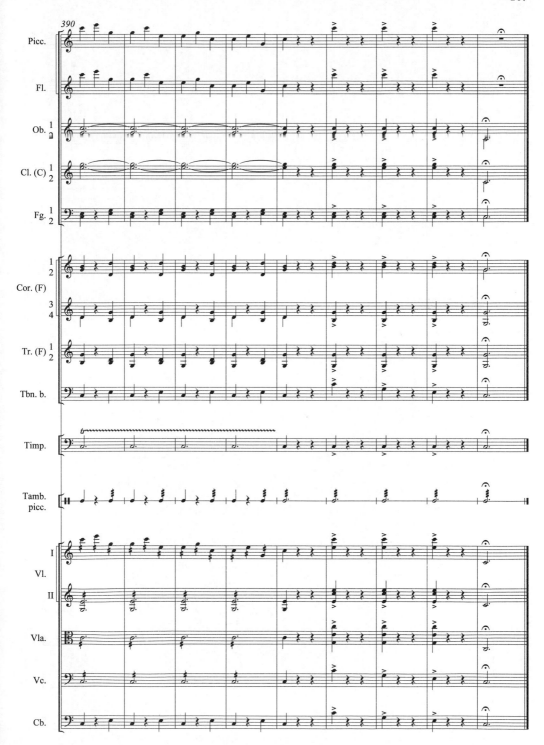